TRANSLATED BY: IGOR GERASIMOV
EDITED BY: CAROLEE KOKOLA
DESIGN: KSENIYA SEMENOVA

ISBN 5-86819-003-3

THE SILVER SAUCER AND THE RIPE, JUICY APPLE

RUSSIAN FOLK TALES

BOOK ILLUSTRATOR OLGA KONDAKOVA

GOLDEN COCKY

*... How charming these folk tales are!
Each of them is a poem!*
A. S. Pushkin

THE WOODEN EAGLE

Once upon a time, there lived a tsar who had many servants. His carpenters, potters, tailors, and other craftsmen were far from ordinary domestic servants. The tsar liked his garments to be tailored and his tableware to be ornamented more elaborately than anybody else's, and he was fond of his extravagantly decorated palace.

Many a talented craftsman was there in the tsar's palace!

In the morning, they would all line up in front of the entrance to the palace and wait for the tsar to come out and give his orders to each of them.

One day, it so happened that a goldsmith waiting for the tsar at the entrance to his palace came across a carpenter. They began to argue about which of them was better in his craftsmanship and whose work required greater skill and ingenuity.

The goldsmith said,

"Your work does not require so much talent because all you do is cut things from wood. Look at the treasures that I have made. Each of them is made from pure gold! No one can take their eyes off them!"

The carpenter answered,

"Not much skill is needed to make a valuable object of gold when the gold itself is of great value. Just try to make a delightful object from mere wood that makes everyone gape with wonder. Then I'll believe that you are a real master in your art."

Long did they argue. Their heated dispute almost led to blows when the tsar came out. After hearing their argument, he grinned and ordered,

"Each of you must demonstrate your skill by creating a golden or wooden object. I'll examine them and decide which of you is the better master."

The tsar gave them one week to complete the work.

For fear of losing his life, neither of them dared to protest. And they went out of the palace separately, both deep in thought about how to surpass the other.

After a week, the masters arrived at the palace and stood in line with the other craftsmen waiting for the tsar to come out, each with a knapsack in his hands.

The tsar came out and said, hiding his smile in his beard,

"Well, my friends, show me your art."

He ordered his servants to call into the chamber both

his wife, the tsarina, and his young son, the tsarevitch.

"Let them look at your work too."

The tsar sat down on a bench with the tsarina, and the tsarevitch stood at their side.

The goldsmith came forward first.

"Please, Your Majesty, order your servants to fetch a large tank full of water."

The servants brought a big tank and filled it with water.

The master untied his knapsack, took out a golden duck, and placed it into the tank of water.

The duck swam around quacking, turning its head from side to side, and preening its feathers as if it were a live bird.

The tsar stood open-mouthed with wonder, and the tsarina exclaimed,

"This duck is alive, not made of gold! The goldsmith has coated a live duck with gold!"

The master was offended.

"I can prove that the duck is not alive! Please, allow me to take it apart and assemble it again."

He took the duck out of the tank and unscrewed and removed first its wings, then its head, and at last completely broke it down into tiny pieces. Then, he reassembled the duck and placed it into the water. The duck swam even better than before.

All the courtiers began to applaud and exclaimed,

"What a master! What a wonder he has created! We have never seen anything like it!"

The tsar turned to the carpenter and said,

"Now it is your turn to show us your work."

The carpenter bowed to the tsar and said,

"Please, Your Majesty, order your servants to open the window in this room."

The servants opened the window.

The carpenter untied his knapsack and took out a wooden eagle. This eagle was made with such skill that it could have easily been mistaken for a real one. The carpenter then said,

"The golden duck can only swim in water, but my eagle can fly up in the sky."

The carpenter mounted his eagle and turned a knob. In an instant, the eagle flew out of the tsar's chamber. All those present in the chamber rushed to the window with their mouths agape, and saw the carpenter flying loops and circles over the tsar's palace courtyard. When the knob was turned to the left, the eagle descended; when it was turned to the right, it soared up high. The tsar, having pushed his crown to the back of his head in wonder, continued to stare out of the window, unable to keep his eyes off the sight.

Everyone around stood dumbfounded. None of them had ever seen such a masterpiece. Having performed a few loops in the sky, the carpenter returned and landed in the chamber. He put the eagle aside and came up to the tsar.

"Well, Your Majesty, are you satisfied with my work?"

"I cannot find the words to express my satisfaction," answered the tsar. "But how have you managed to create such a wonder?"

Hardly had the carpenter begun to explain his invention to the tsar, when the tsarina gasped in terror,

"Where are you going?! Someone catch him! Stop him!"

Everyone in the room turned to her and saw what had happened: as the tsar asked the carpenter his question, the young tsarevitch mounted the eagle, turned the knob, and flew out of the window into the courtyard.

"Come back immediately! You'll kill yourself!" shouted the tsar and the tsarina in horror. But the

tsarevitch waved in farewell and flew over the silver fence enclosing the palace.

He turned the knob to the right, and the eagle climbed up through the clouds and vanished out of sight.

The tsarina fainted away and the tsar became infuriated with the carpenter.

"You have devised this thing especially to kill our only son! Guards, catch him and throw him in prison! Unless the tsarevitch comes back within two weeks, hang him on the gallows."

The palace guards caught the carpenter and threw him into a dark cell in the dungeon.

In the meantime, the tsarevitch flew further away from the palace. He enjoyed this flight immensely. There was so much light and space around him! The wind sang in his ears, his curled hair flew in the wind, the clouds quickly swept past under his feet, and the tsarevitch felt as though he were a real bird! He could turn wherever he wished as he soared in the sky!

In the evening, he landed at the outskirts of an unknown town in an unknown tsardom. As soon as he landed, he saw a small wooden house. The tsarevitch knocked at the door, and an old woman leaned out of the window.

"Please, old woman, allow me to stay here for a night, because I am a stranger here and know not a single person with whom I may stay."

"Please, come in, my son," answered the old woman. "There is plenty of room because I live here alone."

The tsarevitch took apart the eagle, put it in his bag and entered the old woman's house. While the old woman prepared dinner for the tsarevitch, he asked her what the name of the town was where he had landed, what kind of people lived there, and what wonders there were in the town.

"There is one wonder in our tsardom, my son," said the old woman. "In the very center of the town is the tsar's palace and next to it is a high tower. This tower is locked by thirty locks and its gate is guarded by thirty guards. No one is permitted to enter the tower. They say that the tsar's daughter lives there. Right after the tsarina gave birth to the girl, she was locked together with her nurse in the tower lest anybody see her. The tsar and the tsarina are afraid that the tsarevna will fall in love with someone and that they may have to let her go for good to a foreign land. They love her too much to part with her. She is their only child. And so, the girl lives locked in the tower."

"Is she beautiful?" asked the tsarevitch.

"I don't know, my son, I've never seen her with my own eyes, but people say that she is by far the most beautiful girl they've ever seen."

The tsarevitch was aflame with the desire to get into the locked tower. He pondered over how he could get to see the tsarevna. The next day, when night fell upon the town, he mounted the wooden eagle, soared up in the sky, and flew to the tower. He directed his eagle towards the only window in the tower.

Once the eagle brought the tsarevitch to the tower, he knocked at the window. The tsarevna was astonished at the sight of the handsome young man.

"Who are you, young man?" she asked.

"Open the window and I will explain everything," he answered.

The tsarevna opened the window and the wooden eagle flew into the room. The tsarevitch dismounted from the eagle, introduced himself, and told the tsarevna who he was and how he had gotten there.

They sat together, unable to keep their eyes off each

other. The tsarevitch asked the tsarevna whether she would marry him.

"I agree," said the tsarevna, "but I fear that my father and my mother will forbid me to marry you."

But the wicked nurse who guarded the tsarevna overheard their secret. She ran to the palace and revealed what she had heard, adding that the tsarevitch was hiding in the old woman's house. In no time, the guards rushed to the house, caught the tsarevitch and dragged him to the palace. There, the tsar sat in his throne, beside himself with rage and pounding his cane on the floor.

"You scoundrel, how dare you violate the tsar's orders? I'll order my guards to execute you tomorrow!"

They cast the tsarevitch into the dungeon and secured all the prison locks. It was announced that the daredevil youth who had secretly entered the tsarevna's tower would be executed.

The next day the gallows were set up, the executioner prepared to do his job, and the tsar arrived with the tsarina to watch the execution.

The tsarevitch was sent to the square. He then turned to the tsar and said,

"Your Majesty, please, grant me a last request."

"Well, what is your wish?"

"Please order your messenger to fetch my bag from the old woman's house."

The tsar could not deny the tsarevitch his last request and ordered the messenger to bring the bag.

In the meantime, the executioner had already brought the tsarevitch to the gallows and stood him on the platform. The messenger ran up and gave the tsarevitch the bag.

The tsarevitch opened the bag, jumped up on the wooden eagle - and off he went! He hovered over the

gallows, then soared over the tsar and the crowd assembled.

"Catch him! Don't let him fly away!" shouted the tsar.

The tsarevitch directed his eagle to the familiar window in the tower, took the tsarevna in his arms, and flew away.

"There's no need to be afraid of them catching us now," he said.

The eagle rushed them away to the tsarevitch's tsardom. And there, for nearly two weeks, the wretched carpenter had been suffering in the dungeon, unable to take his eyes off the sky in hope of the tsarevitch's return. The following day was the day that the carpenter would be hanged if the tsar's son did not return. Suddenly, he saw the wooden eagle flying towards the palace and carrying not only the tsarevitch, but also the beautiful tsarevna. The eagle landed in the courtyard. The tsarevitch helped his bride dismount from the eagle and introduced her to his father and his mother. He explained where he had been the past two weeks. The tsar and the tsarina were so relieved and happy to see their son that they forgave him for making them worry and ordered their servants to let the carpenter free. The tsar arranged a magnificent marriage feast for the tsarevitch and his bride. The wedding celebrations lasted for three months.

THE COPPER, SILVER, AND GOLDEN TSARDOMS

Once upon a time there lived a tsar. He had a wife named Nastasya and three sons, Tsarevitch Pyotr, Tsarevitch Vasily, and Tsarevitch Ivan. One day, the tsarina went out for a walk in the garden with her nurses and the ladies of the court. All of a sudden, a great Whirlwind rushed in, caught the tsarina, and swirled away. The tsar was grief-stricken and didn't know how to save the tsarina. When the tsarevitches grew older, he asked them, "My dear sons, which of you will go search for your mother?" The two elder brothers resolved to find the tsarina and set off.

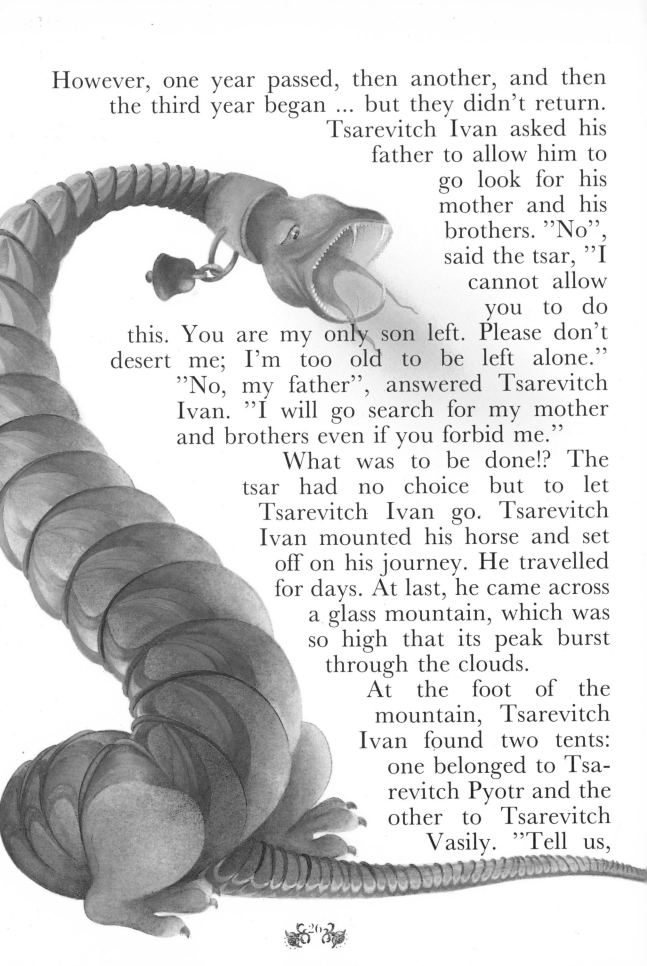

However, one year passed, then another, and then the third year began ... but they didn't return. Tsarevitch Ivan asked his father to allow him to go look for his mother and his brothers. "No", said the tsar, "I cannot allow you to do this. You are my only son left. Please don't desert me; I'm too old to be left alone." "No, my father", answered Tsarevitch Ivan. "I will go search for my mother and brothers even if you forbid me."

What was to be done!? The tsar had no choice but to let Tsarevitch Ivan go. Tsarevitch Ivan mounted his horse and set off on his journey. He travelled for days. At last, he came across a glass mountain, which was so high that its peak burst through the clouds.

At the foot of the mountain, Tsarevitch Ivan found two tents: one belonged to Tsarevitch Pyotr and the other to Tsarevitch Vasily. "Tell us, please, dear Ivanushka", asked his brothers, "where you are going." "I've been looking for my mother and for you, my brothers!" answered Tsarevitch Ivan.

"Oh, Tsarevitch Ivan," said the brothers, "we found our mother's traces long ago, but have been trying to climb up the mountain for three years!"

"Let me try, my brothers."

Tsarevitch Ivan began to climb up the slippery glass mountain. But for every two steps he crawled up, he slid back down one step. Tsarevitch Ivan climbed up the mountain for two days. His hands were scratched by the jagged rocks and his legs were bleeding. At last, on the third day, he reached the top of the mountain. He shouted down to his brothers, "I'll go search for our mother! Wait for me down there for three years and three months! If I don't return before then, it will be pointless to wait any longer. Even the crows will not be able to bring back my bones."

After a short rest, Tsarevitch Ivan began to walk along the crest of the mountain. He walked and walked, and finally came to a copper palace. The gate of the palace was guarded by dreadful fire-breathing dragons that were shackled to it with copper chains. A copper well stood near the gate, with a copper bucket hanging from a copper chain. The dragons strained at their chains as they tried to reach the water, but the chains were too short.

Tsarevitch Ivan took the bucket, scooped out some cold water and gave it to the dragons. The dragons calmed down and Tsarevitch Ivan entered the palace. There he was met by the tsarevna of the copper tsardom.

"Who are you, brave man?" she asked.

"I am Tsarevitch Ivan," he replied.

"Why have you come to my palace?"

"I'm looking for my mother, Tsarina Nastasya," Tsarevitch Ivan replied. "She was stolen away by the Whirlwind. Do you know where I can find her?"

"I don't know. But my elder sister lives not far from here, and maybe she'll be able to tell you where your mother is," said the tsarevna of the copper tsardom, and she gave him a copper ball.

"Roll the ball," she said, "and it'll lead you to my elder sister. And if you defeat the Whirlwind, please take me with you to the free world."

"Agreed," said Tsarevitch Ivan. He dropped the ball, the ball rolled forward, and Tsarevitch Ivan followed it.

Soon he came to a silver tsardom. Its gate was guarded by dragons chained by silver chains, and near the gate was a well with a silver bucket.

Tsarevitch Ivan scooped out some water and gave it to the dragons. The dragons quieted down and allowed Tsarevitch Ivan to enter the palace, where he was met by the tsarevna of the silver tsardom.

"For nearly three years," she said, "the mighty Whirlwind has held me here. I have neither seen nor heard from a soul for a very long time, but you have somehow found me. Who are you, brave man?

"I am Tsarevitch Ivan."

"Why have you come to my palace?" asked the tsarevna of the silver tsardom.

"I'm looking for my mother, Tsarina Nastasya. She was stolen away by the Whirlwind. Do you know where I can find her?" Tsarevitch Ivan asked.

"I don't know. But my elder sister, tsarevna Yelena the Beautiful of the golden tsardom, lives not far from here. Maybe she can tell you where you can find your mother. Take this silver ball. Roll it in front of you and

follow it. But if you defeat the Whirlwind, please take me with you to the free world."

Tsarevitch Ivan rolled the silver ball and followed it.

He walked and walked, and finally saw a golden palace glowing as brightly as if it were aflame. The palace gate was guarded by several terrible, fire-breathing dragons shackled with golden chains. Next to the well was a golden bucket tied to a golden chain.

Tsarevitch Ivan scooped out some water and gave it to the dragons. The dragons drank the water and let Tsarevitch Ivan pass. Tsarevitch Ivan entered the palace, where he was met by Yelena the Beautiful, a tsarevna of undescribable beauty.

"Who are you, brave man?" she asked.

He replied, "I am Tsarevitch Ivan, and I'm looking for my mother, Tsarina Nastasya. Maybe you know where I can find her."

"Yes, I know where she is. She lives not far from here. Take this golden ball. Roll it in front of you and follow it: it will lead you to the place you are searching for. And, if you defeat the Whirlwind, please take me with you to the free world."

"Agreed, my beauty," said Tsarevitch Ivan.

The rolling ball showed Tsarevitch Ivan the way. Long did he walk. At last, he saw a palace so incredibly beautiful that its likes had never been imagined even in fairy tales. The magical glow radiated by the palace could only be comparable with the radiance of flawless pearls and perfectly faceted jewels. And the gate of the palace was guarded by hissing six-headed dragons spitting forth flame.

Tsarevitch Ivan gave the dragons water to drink and they allowed him to enter the palace. Tsarevitch Ivan wandered through many huge chambers and, in the farthest room, he at last found his mother. She sat on a high throne, dressed in richly decorated robes, with a jewel-studded crown on her head. When she saw her guest, she exclaimed, "Ivanushka, my son! How on earth did you find your way here?"

"I've been searching for you, my mother, to take you home," he replied.

"I'm afraid, my son, that it will be difficult to save me. The Whirlwind is too mighty. But I think I can help you. I know how to make you stronger."

She led him down to the cellar, where two barrels full of water stood. One was on the right side of the cellar and the other was on the left.

"Ivanushka, drink some water from the right-hand barrel."

Tsarevitch Ivan drank some water.

"How do you feel? Have you become stronger?" asked Tsarina Nastasya.

"Yes, I have, my mother. I feel as if I could knock down the palace with one hand!"

"Drink some more." Tsarevitch Ivan took another gulp.

"How strong do you feel you are now, my son?"

"I feel as if I could spin the entire universe with one hand!"

"That's enough, my son. Now switch the two barrels. Put the barrel on the right side to the left and the one on the left side to the right."

Tsarevitch Ivan switched the barrels.

"The water in the barrel that is now on the left makes one stronger, and the water in the other makes one weaker. When fighting, the Whirlwind drinks the water that makes him stronger. That's why nobody can defeat

him," Tsarina Nastasya explained.

They returned upstairs to the palace. "The Whirlwind will come soon," said Tsarina Nastasya. "As soon as he comes, grab onto his club. And hold tight, lest you lose your grip! He may soar up into the sky, but you must hold on as tightly as you can. He may rush madly over seas, high mountains, and bottomless abysses, but don't let go! When the Whirlwind gets tired, he'll surely want to drink some water to make him stronger, and he will drink from the barrel that is on the right side. You must then drink from the left-hand barrel."

No sooner had she uttered these words than it grew dark and everything in the room began to shake. The Whirlwind rushed into the room. Tsarevitch Ivan ran up to him and grabbed his club.

"Who are you? Where have you come from?" cried the Whirlwind, "I'll eat you up!"

The Whirlwind flew out of the window and soared up in the sky. He flew over seas, high mountains, and bottomless abysses. But Tsarevitch Ivan held tightly onto the club. At last, the Whirlwind was so tired that he couldn't catch his breath, so he descended to the palace and rushed down to the cellar. He flew to the barrel at the right and began to gulp down the water.

Tsarevitch Ivan ran to the barrel on the left side.

The more the Whirlwind drank, the weaker he became, whereas Tsarevitch Ivan grew stronger with every gulp. And, when Tsarevitch Ivan felt powerful enough, he drew a sharp sword and beheaded the Whirlwind with a single chop.

Tsarevitch Ivan heard voices behind him shouting, "Give him another chop! Strike him again! He may come back to life!

"No, there is no need," answered Tsarevitch Ivan. "With such strength only one strike was needed to down my foe."

Tsarevitch Ivan ran to Tsarina Nastasya. "Let's go, mother. My brothers are waiting for us at the foot of the mountain. Besides, we must take the three tsarevnas with us on our way back." And they set forward.

They first returned to the palace of Yelena the Beautiful. She picked up a golden egg and rolled it, and soon the entire golden tsardom was tucked inside this egg.

"I'm so grateful to you, Tsarevitch Ivan," she said, "You've saved me from the Whirlwind. Take this egg and, if you wish, you may become my bridegroom."

Tsarevitch Ivan took the golden egg and kissed the tsarevna on her scarlet lips.

On their way back, they retrieved the tsarevna of the silver tsardom and the tsarevna of the copper tsardom. They brought woven fabric with them and walked to the place where Tsarevitch Ivan ascended the mountain. First Tsarina Nastasya, then Yelena the Beautiful, and then the two tsarevnas slid down the fabric. And there, at the foot of the mountain, Tsarevitch Ivan's two brothers were waiting for them.

When the brothers saw their mother, they were overjoyed. They stood agape at Yelena the Beautiful; however, when they saw Yelena's two sisters, they became jealous of Tsarevitch Ivan.

"Well," said Tsarevitch Vasily, "our Ivanushka has become his elder brothers' leader. Let's take our mother and the tsarevnas to our father, and let our Ivanushka breathe some fresh air up there on the mountain top!"

"That's right," said Tsarevitch Pyotr. "I'll marry Yelena the Beautiful, and you can marry the tsarevna of the silver tsardom. Our general can marry the tsarevna of the copper tsardom."

In the meantime, Tsarevitch Ivan was getting

ready to slide down. But he had hardly begun to tie the fabric to a tree stump when his elder brothers grabbed the end of the cloth and snatched it down from Tsarevitch Ivan's hands. How could he descend now?

Tsarevitch Ivan was left all alone on the mountain. He began to cry bitterly and started to walk around. He walked and walked, but didn't come across a single soul. Tsarevitch Ivan started to swing the Whirlwind's club in anxiety. No sooner had Tsarevitch Ivan tossed the club from one hand to the other than several ugly, lame goblins appeared out of nowhere.

"What do you wish, Tsarevitch Ivan? We can grant you three wishes," they said.

Tsarevitch Ivan replied, "I'm hungry. Please help me, lame and ugly creatures!" As soon as he uttered these words, he found himself at a table full of the most delicious food he had ever seen.

Tsarevitch Ivan ate his fill and again tossed the club from one hand to the other.

"I wish to have a rest!" he ordered. He immediately found himself lying in a carved oak bed, on a mattress filled with swans' feathers, and covered by a silk blanket. When Tsarevitch Ivan woke up after a long nap, he tossed the club for the third time from one hand to the other. The ugly, lame goblins appeared in an instant.

"What do you wish, Tsarevitch Ivan?"

"I wish to be in my tsardom." Tsarevitch Ivan instantly found himself in his tsardom standing dumbfounded right in the center of the market.

Tsarevitch Ivan saw a shoemaker walking towards him, singing a merry tune.

"Where are you going?" asked Tsarevitch Ivan.

"I'm going to sell the shoes I have made."

"Please take me as your apprentice," Tsarevitch Ivan requested.

"Do you know how to make shoes?"

"Oh, I have many useful skills. I not only know how to make shoes, but I can also sew magnificent dresses."

Later, when they returned to the shoemaker's home, the shoemaker said, "Take this piece of fine leather and make shoes from it. We'll see what sort of shoemaker you are."

"You call this rubbish leather!? If I were you, I would throw it in the trash!" Tsarevitch Ivan scoffed.

That night, when everybody in the shoemaker's house was asleep, Tsarevitch Ivan took the golden egg and rolled it ahead of him as he walked along the road.

He soon came to the golden palace. Tsarevitch Ivan entered the chambers, found a pair of golden embroidered shoes in a trunk, and rolled the egg back along the road, hiding the golden palace inside. He put the shoes on the shoe-maker's table and went to bed.

Early the next morning, the shoemaker saw the shoes and exclaimed, "These shoes are suitable only for the courtiers in the tsar's palace!"

In the meantime, preparations were underway in the palace for the three wedding celebrations: Tsarevitch Pyotr was going to marry Yelena the Beautiful, Tsarevitch Vasily — the tsarevna of the silver tsardom, and the general — the tsarevna of the copper tsardom.

The shoemaker brought the shoes into the palace. As soon as Yelena the Beautiful saw the shoes, she understood what had happened.

"I see that Tsarevitch Ivan, my destined bridegroom, is alive and is somewhere in the tsardom," she thought.

She said to the tsar, "Your Majesty, order this shoemaker to sew for me by tomorrow a wedding gown embroidered with golden lace and studded with precious jewels and pearls. Otherwise, I won't marry Tsarevitch Pyotr."

The tsar called in the shoemaker and demanded, "Unless you bring a golden embroidered wedding gown for Yelena the Beautiful by tomorrow, I'll have you executed!"

The shoemaker went home with his grey-haired head lowered, brooding over his wretched fate.

"Do you see what you've done to me?" he said to Tsarevitch Ivan.

"Don't worry!" replied Tsarevitch Ivan. "Go to bed. Everything will be fine in the morning!"

When the shoemaker woke up the next morning, he found a wedding gown sparkling with gold and jewels lying on the table. He grabbed the gown, rushed to the palace, and gave it to Yelena the Beautiful.

Yelena the Beautiful rewarded the shoemaker with fine gifts and ordered,

"By sunrise tomorrow, you must have a golden palace built that rises out of the open sea, encircled by majestic trees that shelter birds glorifying me in song. Otherwise, I'll order to have you tortured and executed!"

Scared to death, the shoemaker went home with his grey-haired head lowered, brooding over his wretched fate.

"See what those shoes of yours have done to me!" he said to Tsarevitch Ivan. "I will be executed tomorrow!"

"Don't worry!" replied Tsarevitch Ivan. "Go to bed. Everything will be fine in the morning!"

When the shoemaker's family fell asleep, Tsarevitch Ivan left the house and walked to the shore of the sea.

He rolled the golden egg and, at once, he saw the golden tsardom standing in the sea with the golden palace towering in the center, a golden bridge extending seven kilometers to the shore, and majestic trees, in which birds perched while singing their beautiful songs.

Tsarevitch Ivan stood on the bridge, driving nails into the handrails, and waited for his beloved to return to her tsardom.

Yelena the Beautiful saw the palace and ran to the tsar.

"Your Majesty, look what's happened in our tsardom!"

The tsar saw the palace and gasped with wonder.

"Order your servants to harness the horses to the golden carriage. I'll go to the palace to marry Tsarevitch Pyotr," said Yelena the Beautiful.

The servants harnessed the horses, and Yelena the Beautiful and Tsarevitch Pyotr rode in the golden carriage over the bridge with golden mileposts secured by golden rings.

On each milepost perched a pigeon and a dove, bowing to each other and saying,

"Do you remember, my dove, who saved the tsarina?"

"I do remember, my darling. Tsarevitch Ivan saved her."

And Tsarevitch Ivan stood near the handrails driving in golden nails.

Yelena the Beautiful cried loudly, "Good people! Hold my horses! I was saved not by the man sitting next to me, but by the man standing near the handrails!"
She took Tsarevitch Ivan's hand, sat him beside her, and rode with him to the golden palace, where they were wed. When they returned to the tsar, they told him the whole truth. The tsar was so enraged that he wanted to have his sons executed, but Tsarevitch Ivan begged the tsar to forgive them. Tsarevitch Pyotr married the tsarevna of the silver tsardom and Tsarevitch Vasily married the tsarevna of the copper tsardom. And all the people of the tsardom were invited to the marvelous wedding feast!

THE SILVER SAUCER AND THE RIPE, JUICY APPLE

Once upon a time, there lived an old man with his old wife. They had three daughters. The two elder daughters were fond of pretty dresses and merry jokes, but the youngest daughter was modest and shy. The elder daughters wore bright, multicolored gowns, velvet slippers, and gold necklaces. However, the youngest daughter, Masha, wore simple dresses, and her only charm was her beautiful braid, which was so long that it even touched the flowers growing in the garden. The elder sisters regarded themselves as fine ladies who considered any kind of work to be a shame, whereas

Masha worked from sunrise to sunset in the house, the field, and the garden. She weeded the vegetable garden, milked the cows, and fed the ducks.

Masha willingly did anything she was asked to do. Her elder sisters ordered her to do the chores that they were supposed to do, and Masha obediently did them without uttering a word of protest.

This was the way in which their lives went on, and it seemed that nothing would change.

One day, the old man decided to take his hay to sell at the market and promised his daughters that he would bring them presents.

"Father, buy me some blue silk for a new gown," said one daughter.

"For me, father, buy some pink velvet," said the other daughter. But Masha kept silent. Feeling pity for her, the old man asked her directly,

"What would you like me to buy for you, Masha?"

"Please, dear father, buy me a ripe apple and a silver saucer."

Masha's sisters practically split their sides with laughter.

"Oh, Masha! You little fool! Our garden is full of apples! Take any one you like from there. What do you need a saucer for? For feeding ducklings?"

"No, my beloved sisters," answered Masha. "I will roll the apple over the saucer and utter the magic words that I learned from an old woman who was grateful to me for giving her a piece of bread."

"Now, daughters," the father said. "Don't laugh at your sister! I'll buy the presents that each of you desires."

Nobody knows how far away the market was or how long it took for the old man to sell his hay, but he finally returned with presents for his daughters.

He gave blue silk to the eldest daughter, pink velvet to the second daughter, and a silver saucer and a ripe, juicy apple to Masha.

Masha's sisters were very pleased with their presents and, laughing at Masha, they began to sew new gowns.

"Well, sit with your apple, little fool!"

Masha sat in the corner and rolled the apple over the silver saucer while singing and chanting,

"Roll, apple, over the silver saucer and show me towns and fields, forests and seas! Show me the peaks of mountains and the beauty of the sky! Show me all my Russia, my motherland."

All of a sudden, everybody in the room heard a silvery chime and the room became aglow with silvery light. The ripe, juicy apple rolled over the silver saucer ... and all the world's towns, all the meadows, all the ships in the seas, the peaks of the mountains, and the beauty of the sky were seen in the saucer! The saucer showed the radiant sun following the

silvery moon, stars dancing in a ring, and swans singing as they floated peacefully on sparkling lakes.

The sisters, almost bursting with jealousy, couldn't keep their eyes off this wonderful sight. They tried to think of something to trade with Masha so they could have the saucer and the apple. But Masha didn't want to trade her saucer and apple. Every evening, Masha played with her saucer and apple, much to her sisters' envy. Finally, the sisters devised a plot to lure Masha into the woods.

"Dearest sister, please go with us to pick strawberries in the woods."

The three sisters went to the woods, but couldn't find a single strawberry. However, Masha had brought her saucer with her, and rolled the apple while singing and chanting,

"Roll, apple, over the silver saucer and show us where the strawberries are growing, where the pink roses are flowering!"

No sooner had she uttered these words than the sisters heard a silvery chime and saw the ripe apple rolling over the silver saucer. The silver saucer showed where strawberries were growing in meadows, where pink roses were sleepily opening their petals, where mushrooms were hiding, where sparkling springs were gushing, and where snow-white swans were singing.

When the wicked sisters saw this, they became green with envy. They found a gnarled branch, with which they beat Masha to death. The sisters buried her under a birch tree and took the saucer and the apple. Toward evening they returned home with baskets full of berries and mushrooms.

"Masha ran away from us," they said to their mother

and father. "We searched all through the forest, but couldn't find her. The wolves must have eaten her."

The father said, "Roll the apple over the saucer, and maybe it will show us where our Masha is."

The sisters became deathly pale, but couldn't disobey their father. They tried to roll the apple over the saucer, but the apple wouldn't roll and the saucer did not show the forests, the fields, the peaks of the mountains, or the beauty of the sky.

It so happened that, at that very moment, a young shepherd who was searching for a sheep that was lost in the forest came across a white birch, under which he saw a small mound with pink flowers growing around it. He found a reed growing among the flowers. The young shepherd cut the reed and made a pipe with it.

He had hardly touched the pipe to his lips when the pipe began to play by itself, singing the words, "Play, pipe! Play to charm the shepherd's ear. They killed me, a poor girl, to take my ripe apple and silver saucer."

The frightened young shepherd ran to the village to tell the people what had happened to him in the forest.

The people gathered around the young shepherd and listened in astonishment. Masha's father ran to hear the shepherd's tale. As soon as he took the pipe in his hands, it began to play and sing,

"Play, pipe! Play to charm my father's ear. They killed me, a poor girl, to take my ripe apple and silver saucer."

The father burst in tears and said, "Young shepherd, lead us to the place where you found this reed!"

The young shepherd led them to the mound under the birch tree, where they saw pink flowers growing. Nightingales perched in the trees and sang sweetly.

The villagers dug up the mound and found Masha lying dead in the grave. Dead, but even more beautiful than alive! Her cheeks were aglow, as though she were merely asleep.

And the pipe played and sang, "Play, pipe! My sisters lured me into the forest and killed me to take my silver saucer and juicy apple. Play, pipe! Dear father, bring some magical water from the tsar's well."

Masha's two sisters paled and began to tremble with fear. They fell to their knees and confessed their crime. They were shackled with iron locks to wait for the tsar's orders.

The old man went to the town to fetch the magical, sparkling water. He walked and walked, and finally reached the town and found the tsar's palace.

As the old man walked up to the palace, the tsar himself came down the stairs! The old man bowed to the tsar and told him what had happened to his daughter.

The tsar said, "Take some magical water from my well. And as soon as your daughter revives, bring her to me with her apple and saucer. And bring her wicked sisters as well!"

The happy old man bowed again to the tsar and hurried back with a glass jug filled with the magical water.

As soon as he sprinkled Masha with the water, she came back to life, and flew like a dove into her father's arms. The people that had gathered around rejoiced.

The old man took his daughters to the town, where he was shown into the tsar's palace.

The tsar entered the chamber, and darted a glance at Masha.

Standing in front of him was a young woman who looked like a flower blooming in the spring, whose eyes were like radiating sunbeams. Tears rolled like pearls down her glowing cheeks.

"Where is your silver saucer and juicy apple?" asked the tsar.

Masha revealed the saucer and apple in her hands and gently rolled the apple over the saucer.

The tsar immediately heard bells chime loudly and he saw in the saucer Russian towns speeding past, regiments in town squares entering into combat formations, and commanders standing in front of the soldiers. And all around was such firing and smoke that nothing more could be seen.

The apple kept rolling over the saucer, and it showed the stormy sea and ships sailing like swans, with flapping banners and firing cannons. The ships were surrounded by so much smoke that nothing more could be seen.

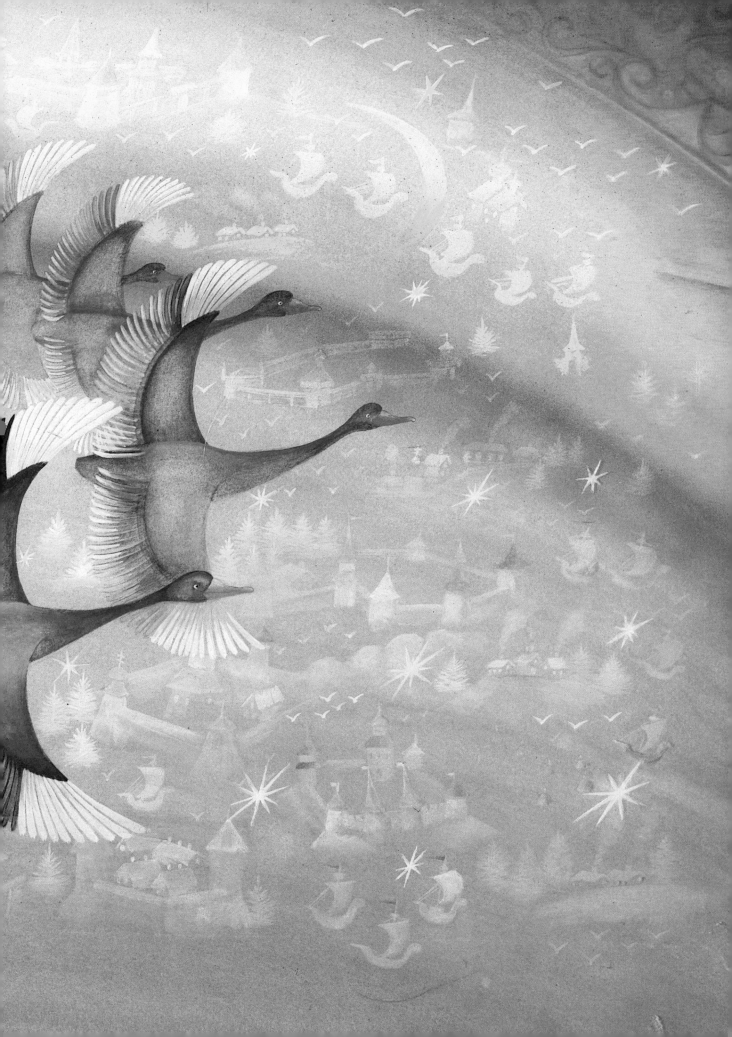

But the ripe apple kept rolling over the silver saucer, which then displayed the blue sky, the radiant sun following the silvery moon, stars dancing in a ring, and swans singing as they floated peacefully on sparkling lakes.

The tsar stood open-mouthed with amazement. Masha, with tears still rolling down her cheeks, said to him,

"Your Majesty, please take the ripe, juicy apple and
the silver saucer, but pardon my sisters. Do not
have them executed for what they've done to
me." The tsar took Masha in his arms and
replied, "I wish you to be my wife and
the good tsarina to my people. I will
pardon your sisters for your sake."
At the wedding feast, there was
such a great celebration
that the stars fell
from the
sky.

JACK FROST

There once lived an old man with his wife. The man had one daughter of his own and his wife had one of her own. The wife loved her daughter tenderly, but disliked her stepdaughter, and forced her to do the lowliest household jobs, scolded her for even the slightest mistakes, and gave her little to eat.

The girl did not refuse to do anything she was ordered. Everyone liked this girl and praised her for her shyness and diligence, but strongly disliked her stepsister because she was lazy and mean. Because of this, the man's wife became even more wicked and quarrelsome. She scolded her stepdaughter all the time. She wanted to ruin the girl completely.

One day the man went to town to shop at the market. His wicked old wife conspired with her daughter to destroy the girl who aroused so much hatred in them.

The stepmother called the girl and ordered, "Go collect firewood in the forest!"

"But we have enough firewood in the house," answered the girl.

The wicked stepmother then began to scold the girl. She stamped her feet and, with the help of her daughter, kicked the girl out of the house.

The girl realized that the stepmother would not allow her back into the house, and she went into the woods despite the bitter frost, howling wind, and whirling snow.

The stepmother and her daughter sat in their warm house and gleefully said,

"She'll never come back! She'll freeze to death in the woods!"

Meanwhile, the girl entered the woods and stopped under a tall fir tree, not knowing what to do....

All of a sudden, she heard a great noise from above and saw Jack Frost hopping from one tree to another, as the branches cracked and shook. Jack Frost climbed down a fir tree and asked, "Glad to see you, fair girl! What has brought you to my forest in such a terrible snowstorm?"

The girl told him that she had come to the forest because she had been thrown out of her home. She told him the whole truth.

Jack Frost listened carefully and said,

"It's not firewood that they've sent you here for. But while you are here, show me what you can do."

He gave her some flax and a spinner and ordered, "Spin threads out of this flax, knit the threads into fabric, and sew me a shirt!"

Jack Frost then disappeared. Without any hesitation, the girl sat down and began to work.

When her fingers became too cold to move, she breathed on them to warm them up and then resumed her work. She worked all night, concentrating on one thing - how to sew a shirt that Jack Frost would be fond of.

In the morning, the girl again heard the loud crackling and Jack Frost suddenly appeared. He examined the shirt and said, "Well done, my girl!"

Jack Frost placed a large steel trunk in front of the girl and said,

"Your reward will match your work!" He then gave the girl a warm fur coat, tied an embroidered kerchief on her head, and showed her the way to the road.

"Goodbye, my dear girl! The good people will help you find the way home."

As soon as he uttered these words, he vanished as if he had never even existed.

In the meantime, the old man came back from the market.

"Where is my daughter?" he asked.

"She went into the woods to collect firewood, and she did not return."

The old man became worried about his daughter and, without unharnessing the horses, he rode to the forest. Just as he entered the forest, he saw his daughter, well-dressed and gay.

The old man sat her in the sledge, put the trunk full of presents in the back of the sledge, and drove home.

Meanwhile, the wicked old woman and her daughter sat at the table eating buns and saying, "Well, she won't return home alive! The old man will bring home only her bones!"

But the dog, lying near the stove, suddenly began to

bark, "Bow-wow, bow-wow! The old man's daughter is bringing wonderful presents home! And no one will marry the old woman's daughter and she'll spend her life alone!"

At first the old woman threw a bun to the dog to calm it down, but then she became angry and hit it with the poker. She scolded, "Shut up, you wretch! You should say, 'The old woman's daughter will be given in marriage, and the old man's daughter will be brought home dead in the carriage!'"

But the dog stubbornly repeated, "The old man's daughter is bringing wonderful presents home! And no one will marry the old woman's daughter and she'll spend her life alone!"

Then the gate squeaked, the door opened, and the well-dressed and rosy-cheeked girl entered the house, with neighbors carrying the huge frost-decorated trunk.

The old woman and her daughter rushed to the trunk and, pulling out the elaborate dresses and textiles and spreading them on the table, they began to inquire about who gave the girl such beautiful gifts.

After learning that the girl received the extravagant presents from Jack Frost, the old woman became excited. She quickly dressed her daughter as warmly as she could, thrust a basket full of buns into her hands, and ordered the old man to take her in the wood.

"She'll bring back two trunks of gifts!" she said, rubbing her hands together with greed.

The old man brought the old woman's daughter into the forest and left her under a tall fir tree. Shivering from the cold and looking around in expectation, she began to grumble.

"Why hasn't Jack Frost come yet? Where is that wretch hiding?"

Suddenly, she heard a crackling sound above her head and saw Jack Frost hopping from one fir tree to another, as the branches cracked and shook. Jack Frost climbed down a fir tree and said, "Glad to see you, fair girl! What has brought you to my forest in such a terrible snowstorm?"

"You know the answer yourself! I've come for wonderful presents!"

Jack Frost grinned to himself.

"First, show me what you can do. Knit me a pair of gloves."

He gave her knitting needles and a ball of yarn and disappeared.

Enraged, the old woman's daughter threw away the knitting needles and kicked away the ball of yarn.

"You old crook! Have you ever seen anyone knit in such a bitter frost? My fingers would freeze!"

In the morning, the girl heard again the loud crackling and saw Jack Frost.

"Well, my fair girl, show me my gloves."

The old woman's daughter shouted,

"What gloves are you talking about, you idiot? You must be blind to not notice that I've nearly frozen to death waiting for you!"

"Well, your reward will match your work," said Jack Frost.

Shaking his beard, he raised such a snowstorm that all the roads and walkways immediately became blocked with snow, and he vanished into thin air as if he had never even existed.

The old woman's daughter, who did not know the way home, lost her way and wandered into a deep ravine, where she was buried in the snow.

The next morning at dawn, the old woman woke up the old man, ordered him to go to the forest to bring her daughter back home and began baking buns. But the dog sitting under the bench began to bark,

"Bow-wow, bow-wow! Soon the old man's daughter will be given away in marriage, but to come out of the woods the old woman's daughter is unlikely to manage!"

At first the old woman threw the buns to the dog to calm it down, but then she became angry and hit it with the poker. She scolded, "Shut up, you wretch! You should say, "The old woman's daughter will bring dear presents in the carriage, and the old man's daughter will never be given away in marriage."

But, after he ate each bun, the dog barked again and again, "Bow-wow, bow-wow! The old man's daughter will find a handsome young beau, but the old woman's daughter will be lost in the snow!"

The old woman was alarmed. "I hope my daughter is safe and sound! I hope she hasn't lost her presents! I'd better follow the old man!"

She put on her fur coat and ran toward the forest. In the meantime, the wind was howling even louder and the snow was swirling even faster. The road was covered with snow.

The wicked old woman lost her way and was buried in the snow. The old man wandered through the forest in search of the old woman's daughter in vain. When he returned home, his wife was missing as well. He gathered all his neighbors, and they searched for the old woman and her daughter. They searched through the forest, and dug out every snowdrift, but couldn't find them.
Since then, the old man and his daughter lived in the house. When the spring came, a handsome young man - the village blacksmith - asked for her hand.
They celebrated their wedding and began
to live in love and harmony.
They are living
so even
now.

CONTENTS

THE SILVER SAUCER AND THE RIPE, JUICY APPLE

Printed by «Detskaya Kniga» RUSSIA